What Do You Do?

First published in Great Britain by HarperCollins Children's Books in 2005
First published in paperback in 2010

1 3 5 7 9 10 8 6 4 2

ISBN: 978-0-00-735353-8

HarperCollins Children's Books is a division of HarperCollins Publishers Ltd.

Text and illustrations copyright © Mandy Stanley 2005

The author/illustrator asserts the moral right to be identified as the author/illustrator of the work.

The HarperCollins website address is: www.harpercollins.co.uk

Printed in China

What Do You Do?

BY MANDY STANLEY

HarperCollins *Children's Books*

Hey, hen! What do you do?

I lay eggs.

Wow, cow! What do you do?

I give milk.

Gee, bee! What do you do?

honey

I make honey.

So, snail! What do you do?

I carry my house on my back.

...a butterfly!

Excuse me, elephant! What do you do?

I squirt water.

Golly, glow-worm! What do you do?

I light up in the dark.

Let's have a word, bird! What do you do?

I build nests.

Aha, cheetah! What do you do?

I run fast.

So tell us, beetle!

What do **YOU** do?

Are you ready?

I ROCK!

That's what I do!

What do YOU do?

Also look out for these fabulous books
by Mandy Stanley!

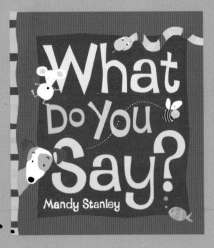

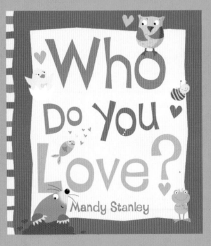

Paperback: 978-0-00-664778-2
Board Book: 978-0-00-714604-8

Paperback: 978-0-00-718406-4
Mini HB: 978-0-00-729342-1

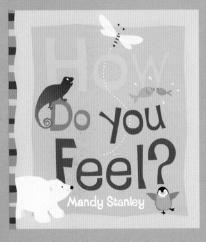

Board Book: 978-0-00-716578-0

Winner of
the Booktrust
Early Years
Baby Book
Award 2006